LAND OF THE PYRAMIDS

The pyramids of Egypt are among the most famous buildings in the world. For more than 2,500 years, people have travelled to Egypt to marvel at these huge, mysterious desert monuments, and each year thousands of visitors still come from all over the world to see them.

W9-BYN-185

There are at least eighty pyramids still standing in Egypt, but there must have been many more in ancient times. Most of the pyramids were built as royal tombs, and nearly all of them are in the cemeteries of Egypt's ancient capital, Memphis.

Memphis was founded in about 3200 BC, when Egypt first became one country. Egypt is a hot, dry land in the north-east of Africa, and life in ancient Egypt depended on the River Nile.

Most ancient Egyptians lived in villages and towns along the Nile. Memphis was built where the river begins to spread out into many branches before it enters the Mediterranean Sea, creating a huge triangular area of fertile land called the Nile Delta. South of Memphis, in the Nile Valley, the fertile land is just a narrow strip along the river bank.

DID YOU KNOW?
Medieval travellers to Egypt called the pyramids 'Joseph's Granaries'. They thought they were where the ancient Egyptians had stored grain to last through times of famine.

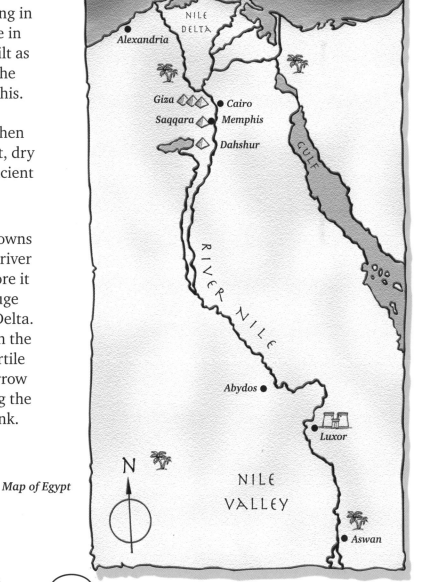

Map of Egypt

THE KING

The king was the most important person in ancient Egypt. People believed that he was the son of the gods, and that he had divine powers. Statues of dead kings were worshipped as gods in special temples.

The Egyptians believed that the spirits of their dead rulers travelled through the sky with the sun god Ra. When he rose in the east each morning, their souls were born again; when he set in the west each night, they followed him into the land of the dead.

For the king's spirit to survive in the afterlife, his name and body had to be preserved, and he had to be provided with everything he needed to live - such as food and drink, furniture, clothes, jewellery and cosmetics. His body was mummified to prevent it from decaying, and his name was carved deep into stone monuments.

Statue of King Menkaura from his pyramid at Giza

DID YOU KNOW?

Egyptian kings were sometimes called 'Pharaoh', which means 'Great House'. Great House was another name for the royal palace.

MAKE A ROYAL BEARD

Egyptian kings used to shave their faces, but they wore a false beard as part of the traditional royal dress. Here's how to make your own royal beard.

You will need:
A short cardboard tube
Two long elastic bands
Crayons, felt tips, or metallic foil
Scissors
A hole punch
Sticky tape

1) Cut a V-shaped slit in the cardboard tube, and cross the bottom ends over to make the beard taper. Tape along the cut edges to hold them in place.

2) Decorate the beard with stripes or a plaited design, or try covering it with foil to make it look like gold or silver.

3) Make a hole on either side of the beard, about 1 cm (½ inch) away from the top edge (a hole punch is useful for doing this).

4) Thread one end of a rubber band through one of the holes to make a loop. Push the other end of the band through the loop to hold it in place.

5) Your beard is finished! To wear it, simply loop the ends of the rubber bands around your ears.

ROYAL TOMBS

The Egyptians called tombs 'houses of eternity'. Royal tombs were built to protect the king's body forever. Egyptian cemeteries were located in the desert to protect the tombs from the Nile flood. The cemeteries of Memphis were built to the west of the town, so the spirits of the dead were close to the entrance to the underworld.

This label shows King Den who ruled Egypt around 3000 BC. It comes from his mastaba tomb at Abydos.

The first kings and queens of Egypt were buried in low, rectangular tombs called mastabas. Mastabas looked like small copies of the palaces the rulers had occupied during their lives. Inside the mastaba there was a central burial chamber, surrounded by small rooms for storing all the things the dead king or queen would need for the next life. Sometimes the mastaba was surrounded by tombs for servants who would serve the king or queen in the Afterlife.

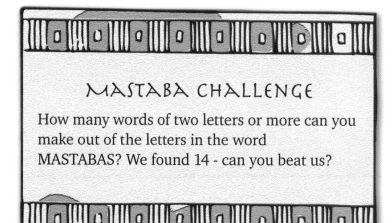

MASTABA CHALLENGE

How many words of two letters or more can you make out of the letters in the word MASTABAS? We found 14 - can you beat us?

DID YOU KNOW?

Mastaba is an Arabic word meaning 'bench'.

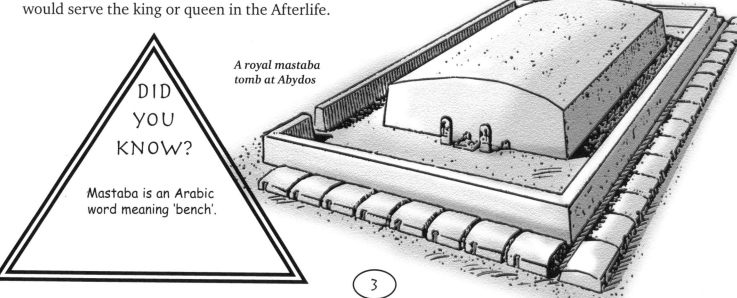

A royal mastaba tomb at Abydos

THE STEP PYRAMID

The first pyramids were built like mastabas with extra levels added on top to make a stepped shape. Nobody knows why the royal architects decided to do this, but many people think this shape was meant to be a staircase that would help the dead king's spirit climb up to heaven to join Ra.

DID YOU KNOW?

The ancient Egyptians thought The Step Pyramid was so amazing that they worshipped its architect, Imhotep, as a god!

JOIN-THE-DOTS PUZZLE

Join the numbered dots in the picture. What do you see?

The Step Pyramid at Saqqara was built for King Djoser around 2650 BC. It is surrounded by chapels and courtyards for the dead king's spirit, and the tombs of his family. The chambers beneath the pyramid are carved with scenes of Djoser performing royal ceremonies.

PYRAMID
PROBLEMS

The Step Pyramid is rectangular, like
a mastaba. Later pyramids were built with
a square base, and the steps were filled in to
give them smooth, triangular sides. Pyramids like
these are called 'true' pyramids.

The royal architects had to experiment
before they were able to build the
perfect pyramid. If the sides were too
steep, the pyramid could
collapse. The Bent Pyramid at
Dahshur, built for King Sneferu
around 2580 BC, looks as if
the builders changed their
minds half-way
through!

DID YOU KNOW?

Every pyramid had
its own name. The Bent
Pyramid was called 'The
Southern Shining Pyramid'.

As well as knowing how to build a pyramid, the
royal architects had to work out how much
stone and how many workers they would need
for the projects. Trainee architects were set
mathematical problems to learn how to make
these calculations.

The Bent Pyramid

Imhotep

WORDSEARCH

There are words hidden in this
pyramid! Can you find and
ring: DESERT, EGYPT, GIZA,
MASTABA, MUMMY,
NILE, PHARAOH,
PYRAMID,
SAQQARA, SKY,
SUN, TOMB.

MUMMIES

The Egyptians believed it was important to preserve the bodies of the dead so they could live again in the afterlife. By the time the pyramids were being built, Egyptian embalmers had discovered how to use a special salt called natron to preserve bodies.

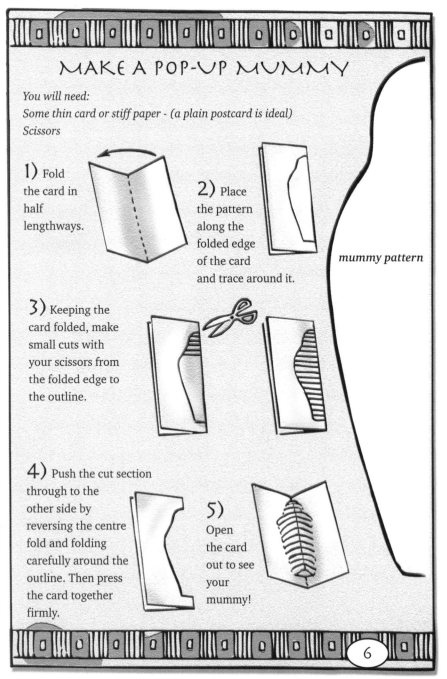

MAKE A POP-UP MUMMY

You will need:
Some thin card or stiff paper - (a plain postcard is ideal)
Scissors

1) Fold the card in half lengthways.

2) Place the pattern along the folded edge of the card and trace around it.

mummy pattern

3) Keeping the card folded, make small cuts with your scissors from the folded edge to the outline.

4) Push the cut section through to the other side by reversing the centre fold and folding carefully around the outline. Then press the card together firmly.

5) Open the card out to see your mummy!

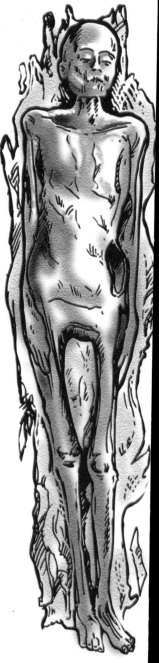

To prepare a body for mummification, the embalmers first removed the internal organs. These were preserved separately in special containers called canopic jars. Then the body was washed and covered with dry natron for forty days. Natron is a disinfectant. It killed all the bacteria that made bodies decay. It soaked up all the fluids in the body and dissolved the fat, but left the skin, bones, muscles, hair, teeth and nails intact. After the body had been dried, the embalmers rubbed the skin with oils and wrapped it in linen bandages.

GODS OF THE DEAD

The Egyptians worshipped many gods and goddesses. Some of them had special responsibility for the dead.

KNOTTED NAMES

These words have got mixed up. Can you unscramble them? Ring the names of gods and goddesses.

ISSI BINUSA KORSA ISORSI
LCJKAA NKGI ESSRIT KHWA
HENSTYPH

Osiris was the first king of Egypt and the ruler of the Underworld. He judged the souls of the dead and decided their fate in the afterlife. **Isis** was the wife and sister of Osiris. She was the goddess of magic and the protector of the dead.

Nephthys was the sister of Isis and Osiris. She helped Isis to protect the dead.

Anubis was the jackal god of cemeteries and mummification.

Sokar was the hawk-headed god of the Memphis cemeteries.

Osiris

Nephthys

Isis

Sokar

Anubis

THE GIZA
PYRAMIDS

The most famous pyramids in Egypt are the three royal pyramids at Giza. All three were built between about 2600 and 2500 BC. The biggest is the Great Pyramid of King Khufu. Measuring 146 m (480 ft) high, its sides were covered with gleaming white polished limestone, and the capstone at the very tip was covered with gold to reflect the rays of the sun. The pyramid of his son King Khafra is a tiny bit smaller, but it was built on higher ground, so it looks bigger. It was guarded by a huge mythical creature, called a sphinx, carved from the desert rock. The smallest of the Giza pyramids was built for Khafra's son King Menkaura. It is only 65 m (213 ft) high, and was never finished.

The kings were not the only ones buried in the royal cemeteries at Giza. The royal pyramids were surrounded by smaller pyramids where the kings' wives and daughters were buried, and by the mastaba tombs of royal relatives and important officials.

DID YOU KNOW?

Engineers surveying the Great Pyramid in the 18th century estimated that it contained enough stone to build a wall 3 m (9 ft) high all the way around France!

ACTIVITY BOX

Here are two pictures of the Giza pyramids - but they are not quite the same! Can you find 5 differences between them?

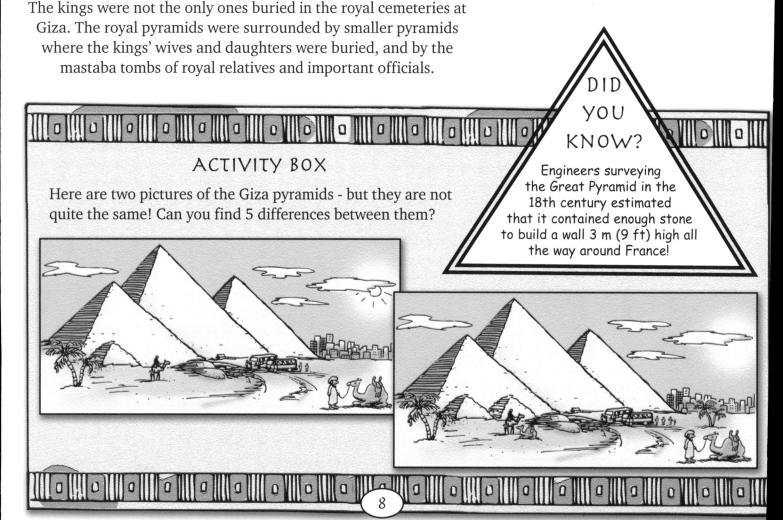

THE SPHINX

The Great Sphinx that guards King Khafra's pyramid is 73 m (240ft) long, and 20 m (66 ft) high. It was carved from the stone left behind by the pyramid-builders.

The Sphinx shows the king with a lion's body. The ancient Egyptians worshipped the Sphinx as a form of the sun god, and built temples in front of it. A carved stone between the Sphinx's front paws tells the story of a prince who dreamed that the Sphinx told him he would become king if he cleared the sand away from its body. After he woke, the prince did as the Sphinx asked. Later he became King Thutmose IV.

MAKE A ROYAL HEADCLOTH

The Sphinx has the head of King Khafra, wearing a royal headcloth. Originally it had a beard like the one on Khafra's statue, but this has been broken off. Here's how to make a headcloth to wear with your royal beard:

1) Take a piece of striped cloth – a tea towel will do.

2) Drape it over your head so the long edge comes just above your eyebrows.

3) Tuck this edge behind your ears and let the ends of the cloth fall forward over your shoulders. Hair clips or a few stitches will hold it in place.

PYRAMID
TEMPLES

The royal pyramid was just part of a huge complex of buildings designed to protect the dead king and help him on his journey into the afterlife.

When the king died, his mummified body was brought by boat to a riverside temple called the Valley Temple, where the funeral ceremonies were held. After this, his body was taken to be buried inside the pyramid along a covered passageway called a causeway. Beside the pyramid was another temple called the Mortuary Temple. Here priests came every day to pray for the dead king's spirit and make offerings of food, drink and sweet-smelling incense to sustain him in the next world.

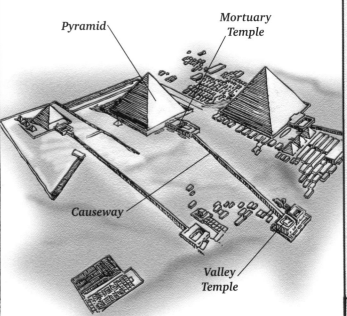

Pyramid

Mortuary Temple

Causeway

Valley Temple

COCONUT PYRAMIDS

The ancient Egyptians didn't have coconuts, but these delicious sweets make an offering fit for a Pharaoh!

You will need:
Desiccated coconut
Icing sugar
Small can sweetened condensed milk
Yellow food colouring (if you like)
Scales
Mixing bowl
Large spoon for mixing
Plates or trays
Can opener

1) Weigh out 250g (8oz) icing sugar and put it in the bowl. Use the spoon to break up any lumps in the sugar.

2) Weigh out 170g (5oz) coconut and add it to the bowl. Stir the coconut and sugar together until they are well mixed.

3) Add some of the condensed milk, a spoonful at a time, until the mixture becomes a stiff paste, like modelling clay.

4) If you like, add a few drops of yellow food colouring and mix it in until the mixture is evenly coloured.

5) To shape the pyramids, first take a piece of the mixture and roll it between your hands to make a ball about 4cm (1½ inches) across. Then gently mould it into a pyramid shape. (Useful tip: a little icing sugar on your hands will stop the mixture sticking to them.)

6) Sprinkle some icing sugar on to a plate. Gently tap each side of the pyramid in the sugar to straighten it. Put the pyramid on a plate or tray.

7) Repeat with the rest of the mixture. Then put the plates or trays of sweets in the fridge for at least 2 hours to harden. Yum!

FUNERAL BOATS

The boats used in royal funerals were
buried in pits around the king's pyramid.

One of King Khufu's boats has been
excavated and reconstructed. If you visit Giza,
you can see it displayed in a special museum beside the Great
Pyramid. Khufu's boat measures 43 m (141 ft) long and was built
of cedar wood brought all the way from Lebanon. It has oars for
rowing, a cabin, and two big steering oars at the stern.

MAKE AN EGYPTIAN BOAT

The design of Khufu's boat was copied from the reed boats
that Egyptians used for travelling on the River Nile. To make
your own Egyptian boat, all you need is a handful of
drinking straws, some thread and a pair of scissors.

1) Take three straws and fold them in half.

2) Pinch the open end of the bundle together and tie yarn around it tightly. Then do the same with the other end.

3) Spread the bundle out to make a flat boat shape.

4) Take six straws and lay them alongside the bundle, three on each side. Bend them around the bundle and tie them at either end.

5) Wrap yarn around the middle part of the boat in a few places. The thread should be tight enough to hold the straws together, but not so tight that they bunch up.

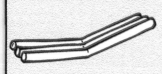

6) Bend the ends of the boat up and tie them tightly. If you need to, you can trim the ends with the scissors.

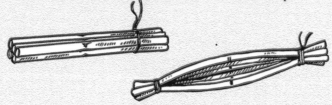

7) Your boat should now be ready to sail - if it tips over, simply adjust the straws until it sits level on the water. When you get good at making these boats, you can try adding a matchbox cabin and toothpick oars!

INSIDE THE
PYRAMID

The heart of every pyramid was the royal burial chamber, where the king's mummified body lay inside a sarcophagus carved from a solid block of stone. The sarcophagus was much bigger than the entrance to the chamber, so it had to be put in while the pyramid was being built.

Pyramids were designed to protect the king's body for ever, and some pyramids had mazes of passages and chambers inside to confuse anyone who tried to break in. After the king was buried, the passages were blocked with huge slabs of stone.

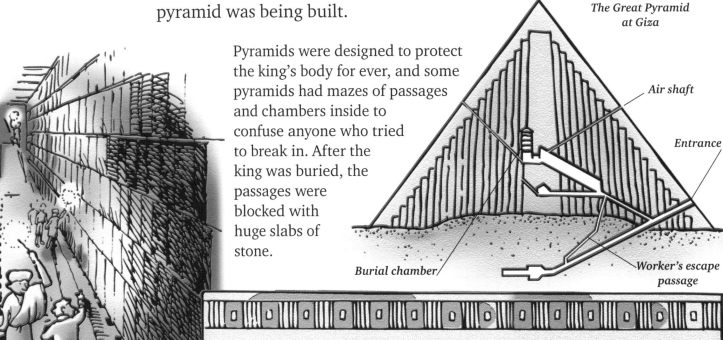

The Great Pyramid at Giza

Air shaft

Entrance

Burial chamber

Worker's escape passage

DID YOU KNOW?

The word 'sarcophagus' is Greek, and means 'flesh-eating'. The Greeks noticed that limestone sarcophagi made unmummified bodies decay faster.

BEWILDERING BANDAGES

Can you tell which bandage the king's mummy has to follow to find his way back to his sarcophagus?

A

B

C

PYRAMID TEXTS

In some pyramids the walls of the burial chamber were carved with magic spells called Pyramid Texts. The Egyptians believed that the king would need his name to survive in the next world. The Pyramid Texts were meant to preserve the dead king's name and to help and protect him in the afterlife.

The Pyramid Texts were written in picture signs called hieroglyphs. The Egyptians believed that hieroglyphs had their own magic power and could come alive, so they were careful not to use signs showing dangerous animals or anything that might hurt the king.

The Egyptians thought that the spirit of the dead king would fly up to the sky to join the sun and the stars. One of the Pyramid Texts in the burial chamber of King Unas at Saqqara says: 'Unas comes, an indestructible spirit, like the morning star'. In decorated burial chambers, the ceiling is usually carved with a beautiful pattern of stars to represent the sky.

SEEING STARS

The artists who decorated the royal burial chamber used a grid to create the starry pattern on the ceiling. You can use this grid to copy them.

PYRAMID BUILDING

The first pyramids were built of stone blocks, covered or 'cased' with white limestone. The surface was polished to make the pyramid shine in the sun. The capstone at the very top was a small pyramid covered with gold to reflect the sun's rays.

Before the builders could start work, they had to make sure the ground was level. They did this by cutting a grid of trenches into the rock and filling them with water. Any stone above the water level was cut away to leave an even surface.

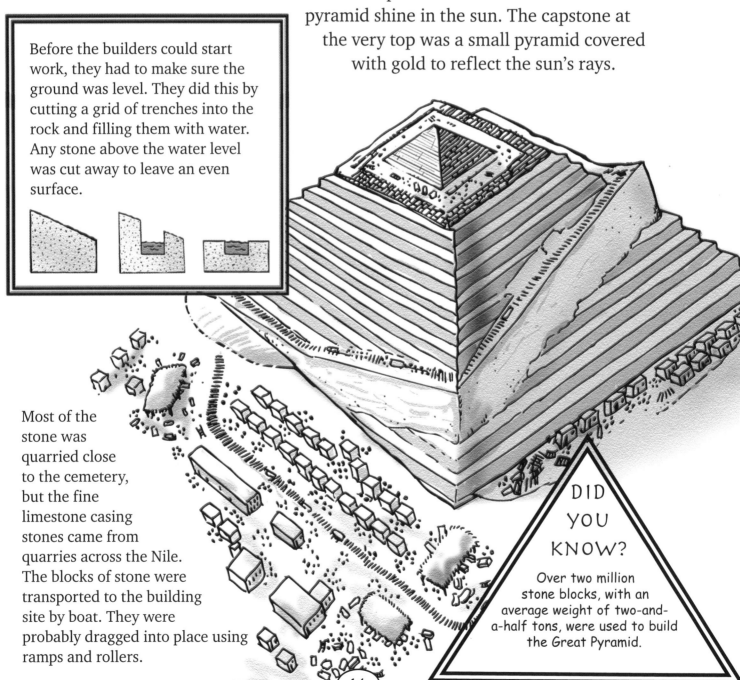

Most of the stone was quarried close to the cemetery, but the fine limestone casing stones came from quarries across the Nile. The blocks of stone were transported to the building site by boat. They were probably dragged into place using ramps and rollers.

DID YOU KNOW?

Over two million stone blocks, with an average weight of two-and-a-half tons, were used to build the Great Pyramid.

PYRAMID
BUILDERS

Thousands of workers were needed
to build a pyramid.

Architects and scribes were needed to choose the building site, design the pyramid, work out how much stone was required, and organize the workforce. There were quarrymen to cut the stone, boatmen to transport it and masons to shape it. Finally, there were the armies of labourers who had to haul the stones into place. Most of the unskilled labourers were farm workers who had no work to do during the annual Nile flood.

All these people needed food and shelter while they were working on the pyramid. They lived in temporary villages, which had huge kitchens and bakeries to feed everyone. It could take up to twenty years to finish a pyramid, so some people spent their whole lives in these towns and were buried in tombs there.

BUILD A PYRAMID

You will need:
Thin card
Scissors
Glue
Paints, crayons or felt tips

1) You'll find a larger version of this pattern inside the front cover of the book. Copy the pattern on to card. You can make your pyramid bigger or smaller if you can photocopy the pattern.

2) Cut carefully around the outside of the pattern or photocopy.

3) Score along the lines to make it easier to fold your pyramid into shape. Fold the sides upwards and inwards so they meet in the centre.

4) Glue tab A to A, tab B to B and so on. If you leave one set of tabs unglued, you will be able to store treasures inside the pyramid.

5) Colour your pyramid.

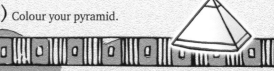

RIDDLES
OF THE
SPHINX

Try these Egyptian jokes on your friends!

Q Why can't you starve in the desert?
A Because of the sand-which-is there!

Q Why was the young Pharaoh confused?
A Because his daddy was a mummy!

Q What did it say on the Pharaoh's door buzzer?
A Toot and come in!

Q Why did the camel look grumpy?
A Because he had the hump!

Q How do you catch a mummy?
A Hide behind a sand dune and make a noise like a pyramid!

Q Why was the archaeologist miserable?
A Because his career was in ruins!

ANSWERS

Page 3
As, am, at, ma, ta, ass, baa, bat, mat, tab, bass, mass, mast, stab.

Page 5

Page 7
Isis, Anubis, Sokar, Osiris, Jackal, King, Sister, Hawk, Nephthys

Page 8

Page 12

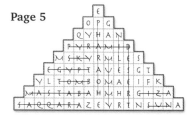

© 2003 The Trustees of The British Museum

Published in 2003 by The British Museum Press
A division of The British Museum Company Ltd
46 Bloomsbury Street, London WC1B 3QQ

ISBN 0 7141 3024 9
A catalogue record for this title is available
from the British Library

Delia Pemberton has asserted the right to
identified as the author of this work

Design, back cover game, and all black and
white illustrations by HERRING BONE DESIGN
Front cover illustration by Frances Button

Printed and bound in the UK by
Ebenezer Baylis & Son Ltd